Nimble
with
Numbers

Student Practice Book

Grade 2

Leigh Childs and Laura Choate

Dale Seymour Publications®
Parsippany, New Jersey

Acknowledgements

Thanks to Maryann Wickett, a special friend, who helped refine these activities with her students and who gave valuable feedback and suggestions.

Dale Seymour Publications
An imprint of Pearson Learning
299 Jefferson Road, P.O. Box 480
Parsippany, NJ 07054-0480

www.pearsonlearning.com

1-800-321-3106

Art Director: Jim O'Shea
Production/Manufacturing Director: Janet Yearian
Production/Manufacturing Manager: Karen Edmonds
Production/Manufacturing Coordinator: Julie Ryan
Editorial Manager: Elizabeth W. Fernald
Executive Editor: Amy Feldman

ISBN 0-7690-2823-3

1 2 3 4 5 6 7 8 9 10 - ML - 06 05 04 03 02 01

This Book Is Printed
On Recycled Paper

Table of Contents

Dear Student and Family,

How many times do you get zapped in a video game before you get to the next level? How many soccer games do you play before you make a goal? If you're like most people, practice helps you reach your goal. Math is like that, too. You need to practice to get it right.

In this book there are three kinds of activities—games, practice pages, and skill checks. You will play games and complete puzzles while practicing addition, subtraction, and place value. The games in this book are made to be used over and over. You may even play the same game four or five times while working in a section. You'll see that you get better at math each time you play.

The practice pages will help you work faster and do better. You will practice numbers on your own and have fun at the same time. You will also do four skill checks in each section of the book. These skill checks will help you, your teacher, and your family find out how you're doing.

Soon you'll be a whiz with numbers—you just need to practice!

Yours truly,

Leigh Childs   *Laura Choate*

P.S. You'll need digit cards (on page 63) for most games and for some of the practice pages in this book. You might want to cut out the cards and save them to use over and over.

P.P.S. Here's a tip. Keep the cards in an envelope glued to the inside of your book.

Addition Facts

Seeking Sums

Warm-up
What sums can you make by adding any three of these numbers?

3   4   5   6   7

Number of Players: 2

Goal: Make as many target sums as you can.

Materials: *Seeking Sums* gameboard (page 7)
Digit cards (1–6)
18 markers

Game Rules

1. Work with a partner. Pick four digit cards.
Place the cards at the top of the gameboard.

2. Use 2, 3, or 4 of the numbers to make sums through 18.
Cover each of your sums on the board.

3. Make as many sums as you can with the same four digit cards.

4. Mix the cards and start again.

Make It Harder: Use digit cards 1–9.

Don't Forget: Play this game again. It will help you do better on skill checks and other activities in the book.

$$
\begin{array}{r} 6 \\ 1 \\ + 5 \\ \hline 12 \end{array}
\qquad
\begin{array}{r} 2 \\ + 1 \\ \hline 3 \end{array}
$$

$$
\begin{array}{r} 2 \\ 1 \\ 5 \\ + 6 \\ \hline 14 \end{array}
\qquad
\begin{array}{r} 2 \\ + 5 \\ \hline 7 \end{array}
$$

$$
\begin{array}{r} 2 \\ + 6 \\ \hline 8 \end{array}
$$

$$
\begin{array}{r} 1 \\ + 6 \\ \hline 7 \end{array}
$$

5	1
2	6

$$
\begin{array}{r} 6 \\ 5 \\ + 2 \\ \hline 13 \end{array}
\qquad
\begin{array}{r} 1 \\ 5 \\ + 2 \\ \hline 8 \end{array}
$$

$$
\begin{array}{r} 6 \\ 1 \\ + 2 \\ \hline 9 \end{array}
\qquad
\begin{array}{r} 5 \\ + 6 \\ \hline 11 \end{array}
$$

$$
\begin{array}{r} 1 \\ + 5 \\ \hline 6 \end{array}
$$

1	2	③	4	5	⑥
⑦	⑧	⑨	10	⑪	⑫
⑬	⑭	15	16	17	18

Seeking Sums

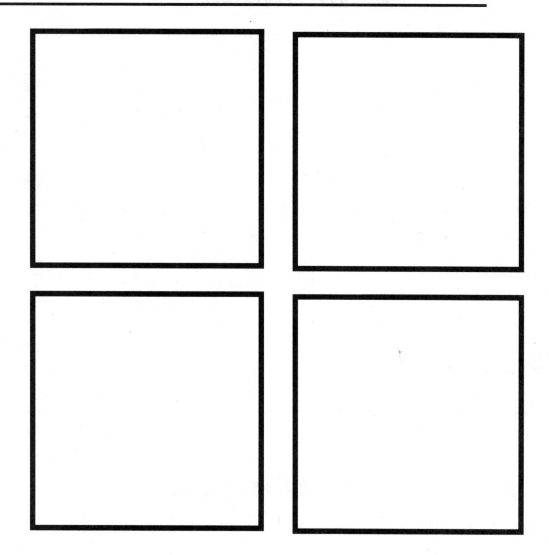

1	2	3	4	5	6
7	8	9	10	11	12
13	14	15	16	17	18

Date _____

Skill Check 1

 Don't start yet! Star two problems that may have answers less than 10.

1. 4
   + 4
   ___

2. 5
   + 3
   ___

3. 7
   + 4
   ___

4. 9
   + 5
   ___

5. $3 + 6 =$ _____

6. $4 + 5 =$ _____

7. $4 + 6 =$ _____

8. $6 + 6 =$ _____

9. $8 + 6 =$ _____

10. $7 + 9 =$ _____

Go On What numbers come next? 2, 5, 8, _____, _____

Date _____

Skill Check 2

 Don't start yet! Star two problems that may have even answers.

1. 5
   + 2
   ___

2. 6
   + 4
   ___

3. 7
   + 6
   ___

4. 9
   + 7
   ___

5. $8 + 2 =$ _____

6. $4 + 7 =$ _____

7. $6 + 5 =$ _____

8. $9 + 3 =$ _____

9. $7 + 7 =$ _____

10. $8 + 8 =$ _____

Go On Write three addition facts that equal 14.

Seeking Sums A

__1__   _____   _____   _____

Look at the sums below. Which sums can be made with the dot cards above?
If you find a way, write the addition fact. The first one is done for you.
Hint: Add 2, 3, or 4 of the dot cards. It is not possible to make every sum.

3 = __1 + 2__   6 = _____   9 = _____

4 = _____   7 = _____   10 = _____

5 = _____   8 = _____   11 = _____

__1__   _____   _____   _____

Look at the sums below. Which sums can be made with the dot cards above?
If you find a way, write the addition fact.
Hint: Add 2, 3, or 4 of the dot cards. It is not possible to make every sum.

4 = _____   9 = _____

6 = _____   10 = _____

7 = _____   11 = _____

8 = _____   12 = _____

Seeking Sums B

1	3	4	6

Look at the sums below. Which sums can be made with the numbers above?
If you find a way, write the addition fact.
Hint: Add 2, 3, or 4 of the numbers. It is not possible to make every sum.

4 = _____   7 = _____   10 = _____

5 = _____   8 = _____   11 = _____

6 = _____   9 = _____   12 = _____

1	2	4	5

Look at the sums below. Which sums can be made with the numbers above?
If you find a way, write the addition fact.
Hint: Add 2, 3, or 4 of the numbers. It is not possible to make every sum.

5 = _____   9 = _____

6 = _____   10 = _____

7 = _____   11 = _____

8 = _____   12 = _____

Independent Activity

Joining Neighbors A

Make each sum. Loop dot cards that are next to each other.
The first one is done for you.

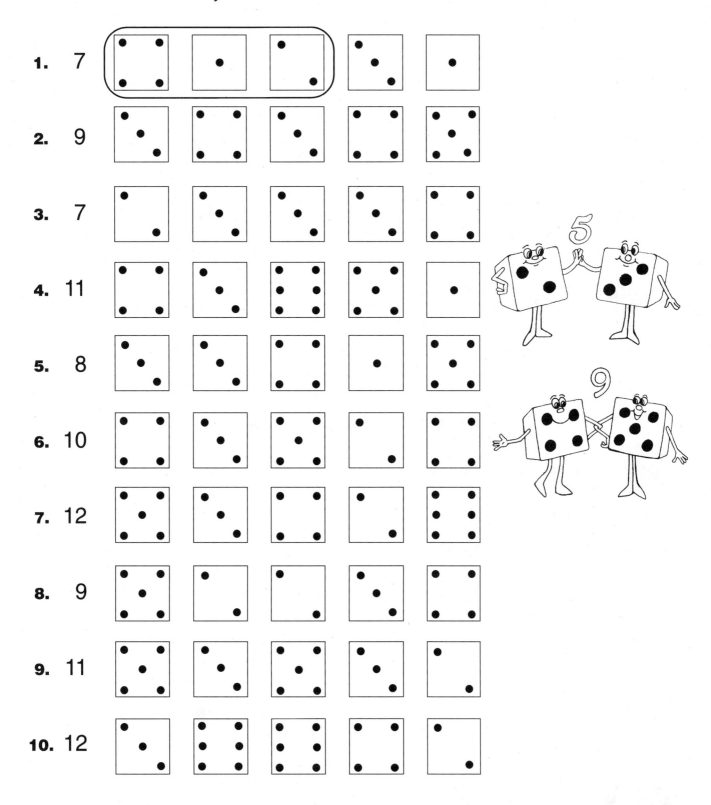

Date _____

Skill Check 3

 STOP Don't start yet! Star two problems that may have answers greater than 15.

1. $\begin{array}{r} 5 \\ +4 \\ \hline \end{array}$
2. $\begin{array}{r} 5 \\ +7 \\ \hline \end{array}$
3. $\begin{array}{r} 8 \\ +5 \\ \hline \end{array}$
4. $\begin{array}{r} 9 \\ +9 \\ \hline \end{array}$

5. $4 + 3 =$ _____

6. $2 + 6 =$ _____

7. $3 + 8 =$ _____

8. $8 + 4 =$ _____

9. $6 + 9 =$ _____

10. $9 + 8 =$ _____

Go On What numbers come next? 1, 5, 9, _____, _____, _____

Date _____

Skill Check 4

STOP Don't start yet! Star two problems that may have odd answers.

1. $\begin{array}{r} 6 \\ +2 \\ \hline \end{array}$
2. $\begin{array}{r} 5 \\ +6 \\ \hline \end{array}$
3. $\begin{array}{r} 7 \\ +7 \\ \hline \end{array}$
4. $\begin{array}{r} 9 \\ +6 \\ \hline \end{array}$

5. $3 + 5 =$ _____

6. $5 + 5 =$ _____

7. $9 + 2 =$ _____

8. $4 + 9 =$ _____

9. $5 + 9 =$ _____

10. $7 + 8 =$ _____

Go On Write three addition facts that equal 15.

Joining Neighbors B

Make each sum. Loop numbers that are next to each other.

1. 9 | 4 | 6 | 3 | 2 | 3 |

2. 11 | 4 | 3 | 5 | 3 | 4 |

3. 10 | 3 | 7 | 6 | 4 | 5 |

4. 13 | 5 | 3 | 6 | 4 | 4 |

5. 12 | 4 | 2 | 5 | 7 | 2 |

6. 12 | 6 | 5 | 3 | 3 | 6 | 1 |

7. 10 | 2 | 3 | 4 | 3 | 1 | 4 |

8. 13 | 4 | 2 | 3 | 4 | 4 | 5 |

9. 12 | 5 | 3 | 4 | 4 | 1 | 5 |

10. 13 | 3 | 4 | 4 | 5 | 2 | 5 |

Joining Neighbors C

Make each sum. Loop numbers that are next to each other. The first one is done for you.

1. (12) 5 4 (7 3 2)

2. (14) 4 2 7 5 4

3. (15) 6 5 4 8 5

4. (14) 6 3 5 1 4

5. (11) 7 2 6 2 3

6. (13) 5 3 4 3 6

7. (13) 5 3 3 4 6

8. (16) 7 5 4 7 7

9. (18) 6 4 3 5 4 3

10. (17) 7 3 4 5 2 6

11. (17) 4 6 8 3 2 5

12. (18) 7 5 7 6 3 6

Sum Triangles A

Make the sum for each side equal the number in the center of the triangle. The first one is started for you.

1.

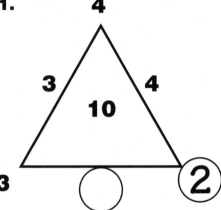

2.

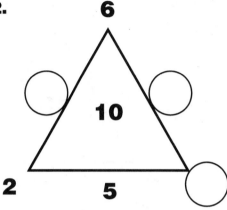

3.

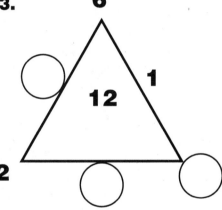

4.

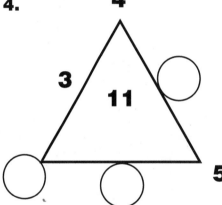

5.

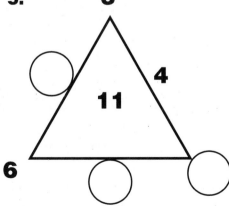

6.

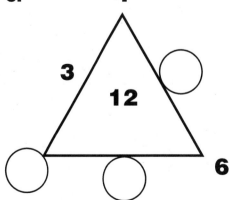

Sum Triangles B

Make the sum for each side equal the number in the center of the triangle.

1.
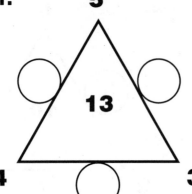

2.
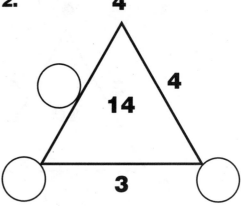

3.
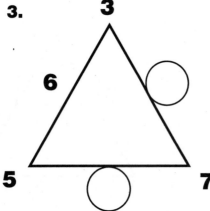

4.
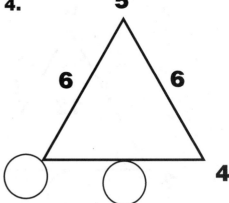

5.
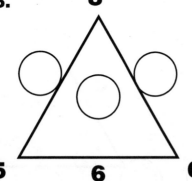

6.
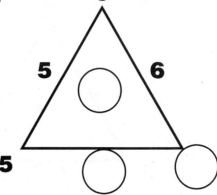

Independent Activity

Subtraction Facts

How Many More?

Warm-up
If you have 5, how many more do you need to make 12?

Number of Players: 2

Goal: Cover three numbers in a row on the gameboard.

Materials: *How Many More to Make 12?* gameboard (page 19)
2 sets of digit cards (2–9 only)
Markers in 2 different colors (12 of each color)

Game Rules

1. Mix the 2 sets of cards.
Stack the cards facedown.

2. For each turn, a player shows the top card.
The player subtracts the number on the card from 12.
The difference is how many more to make 12.
The player covers the difference on the board.

3. Players take turns.

4. The game ends when a player has three counters in a row on the gameboard. That player is the winner.

Make It Harder: Use the *How Many More to Make 15?* gameboard (page 20) and two sets of digit cards (4–9).

Don't Forget: Play the game over and over to help you do better on skill checks and practice pages.

8	7	10	3
6	5	9	4
5	9	10	8
7	4	6	3

How Many More to Make 12?

8	7	10	3
6	5	9	4
5	9	10	8
7	4	6	3

How Many More to Make 15?

10	**8**	**7**	**9**	**11**
7	**6**	**9**	**8**	**7**
11	**9**	**8**	**6**	**9**
6	**7**	**9**	**8**	**10**
8	**11**	**10**	**7**	**6**

8 + ? = 15

Date _____

Skill Check 5

STOP Don't start yet! Star two problems that may have even answers.

1. $8 - 5 =$ _____

2. $10 - 4 =$ _____

3. $11 - 5 =$ _____

4. $13 - 3 =$ _____

5. $7 +$ _____ $= 10$

6. $7 - 2 =$ _____

7. $\begin{array}{r} 9 \\ -6 \\ \hline \end{array}$

8. $\begin{array}{r} 11 \\ -8 \\ \hline \end{array}$

9. $\begin{array}{r} 15 \\ -7 \\ \hline \end{array}$

10. $\begin{array}{r} 17 \\ -8 \\ \hline \end{array}$

Go On What number is missing? 16, 13, 10, _____, 4, 1

Date _____

Skill Check 6

STOP Don't start yet! Star two problems that may have answers less than 5.

1. $7 - 3 =$ _____

2. $9 - 8 =$ _____

3. $12 - 6 =$ _____

4. $14 - 9 =$ _____

5. $8 +$ _____ $= 12$

6. $8 - 5 =$ _____

7. $\begin{array}{r} 10 \\ -8 \\ \hline \end{array}$

8. $\begin{array}{r} 12 \\ -3 \\ \hline \end{array}$

9. $\begin{array}{r} 14 \\ -8 \\ \hline \end{array}$

10. $\begin{array}{r} 16 \\ -8 \\ \hline \end{array}$

Go On $\triangle + \square = 12$
$\triangle - \square = 2$ $\square =$ _____ $\triangle =$ _____

Subtraction Squares A

Subtract each row and column to find the missing numbers.
The first one is done for you.

1.
9	5	*4*
3	1	*2*
6	*4*	*2*

2.
8	4	
5	2	

3.
5	2	
3	1	

4.
7	5	
3	2	

5.
6	3	
4	2	

6.
9	2	
5	1	

7.
9	3	
4	2	

8.
7	4	
5	2	

9.
8	5	
3	3	

Independent Activity

Subtraction Squares B

Subtract each row and column to find the missing numbers.
The first one is done for you.

5 - 2 = 7 - 4 ?

1.

10	5	5
3	1	2
7	4	3

2.

11	4	
6	2	

3.

10	3	
7	1	

4.

12	7	
6	3	

5.

14	6	
7	2	

6.

13	7	
5	3	

7.

15	8	
6	3	

8.

13	6	
4	2	

9.

16	7	
8	4	

Mystery Numbers A

In each problem, $\square$ is one number and $\triangle$ is another number. Find the numbers.

1. $\square + \triangle = 10$

   $\square - \triangle = 2$

   $\square = \rule{2cm}{0.4pt}$

   $\triangle = \rule{2cm}{0.4pt}$

2. $\square + \triangle = 10$

   $\square - \triangle = 4$

   $\square = \rule{2cm}{0.4pt}$

   $\triangle = \rule{2cm}{0.4pt}$

3. $\square + \triangle = 12$

   $\square - \triangle = 6$

   $\square = \rule{2cm}{0.4pt}$

   $\triangle = \rule{2cm}{0.4pt}$

4. $\square + \triangle = 11$

   $\square - \triangle = 1$

   $\square = \rule{2cm}{0.4pt}$

   $\triangle = \rule{2cm}{0.4pt}$

5. $\square + \triangle = 11$

   $\square - \triangle = 5$

   $\square = \rule{2cm}{0.4pt}$

   $\triangle = \rule{2cm}{0.4pt}$

6. $\square + \triangle = 12$

   $\square - \triangle = 2$

   $\square = \rule{2cm}{0.4pt}$

   $\triangle = \rule{2cm}{0.4pt}$

Independent Activity

Date _____

Skill Check 7

 Don't start yet! Star two problems that may have odd answers.

1. $8 - 7 =$ _____   **2.** $10 - 1 =$ _____   **3.** $11 - 7 =$ _____

4. $15 - 6 =$ _____   **5.** $8 +$ _____ $= 11$ **6.** $7 - 6 =$ _____

7. $\begin{array}{r} 9 \\ -5 \\ \hline \end{array}$ **8.** $\begin{array}{r} 12 \\ -8 \\ \hline \end{array}$ **9.** $\begin{array}{r} 13 \\ -4 \\ \hline \end{array}$ **10.** $\begin{array}{r} 17 \\ -9 \\ \hline \end{array}$

Go On ▶ What number is missing? 19, 15, 11, _____, 3

Date _____

Skill Check 8

 Don't start yet! Star a problem that may have the least answer.

1. $7 - 5 =$ _____   **2.** $9 - 4 =$ _____   **3.** $12 - 2 =$ _____

4. $13 - 8 =$ _____   **5.** $4 +$ _____ $= 9$ **6.** $8 - 2 =$ _____

7. $\begin{array}{r} 10 \\ -6 \\ \hline \end{array}$ **8.** $\begin{array}{r} 11 \\ -4 \\ \hline \end{array}$ **9.** $\begin{array}{r} 16 \\ -9 \\ \hline \end{array}$ **10.** $\begin{array}{r} 18 \\ -8 \\ \hline \end{array}$

Go On ▶ $\triangle + \square = 11$
$\triangle - \square = 5$ $\square =$ _____ $\triangle =$ _____

Mystery Numbers B

In each problem, $\square$ is one number and $\triangle$ is another number. Find the numbers.
Hint: All squares on this page are 2-digit numbers.

1. $\square + \triangle = 14$

$\square - \triangle = 8$

$\square = \underline{\hspace{2cm}}$

$\triangle = \underline{\hspace{2cm}}$

2. $\square + \triangle = 17$

$\square - \triangle = 7$

$\square = \underline{\hspace{2cm}}$

$\triangle = \underline{\hspace{2cm}}$

3. $\square + \triangle = 15$

$\square - \triangle = 5$

$\square = \underline{\hspace{2cm}}$

$\triangle = \underline{\hspace{2cm}}$

4. $\square + \triangle = 16$

$\square - \triangle = 8$

$\square = \underline{\hspace{2cm}}$

$\triangle = \underline{\hspace{2cm}}$

5. $\square + \triangle = 18$

$\square - \triangle = 8$

$\square = \underline{\hspace{2cm}}$

$\triangle = \underline{\hspace{2cm}}$

6. $\square + \triangle = 19$

$\square - \triangle = 5$

$\square = \underline{\hspace{2cm}}$

$\triangle = \underline{\hspace{2cm}}$

Independent Activity

Making Equations A

Use 1, 2, and 5 to complete these number sentences.

1. _____ − _____ − _____ = 2

2. _____ + _____ − _____ = 6

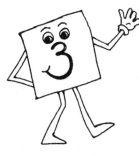

Use 1, 3, and 4 to complete these number sentences.

3. _____ − _____ + _____ = 6

4. _____ + _____ − _____ = 6

Use 1, 3, and 6 to complete these number sentences.

5. _____ + _____ − _____ = 8

6. _____ − _____ − _____ = 2

Use + or − to complete these number sentences.

7. 3 ◯ 1 ◯ 2 = 2

8. 3 ◯ 1 ◯ 2 = 0

9. 6 ◯ 2 ◯ 1 = 7

10. 6 ◯ 2 ◯ 1 = 3

Making Equations B

Use 3, 4, and 8 to complete these number sentences.

1. _____ − _____ + _____ = 7

2. _____ + _____ − _____ = 7

3. _____ − _____ + _____ = 9

Use 5, 7, and 9 to complete these number sentences.

4. _____ + _____ − _____ = 7

5. _____ + _____ − _____ = 3

6. _____ − _____ + _____ = 11

Use + or − signs to complete these number sentences.

7. 8 ◯ 4 ◯ 7 = 11

8. 8 ◯ 4 ◯ 7 = 5

9. 8 ◯ 4 ◯ 7 = 19

Show how many different number sentences you can make using 10, 3, and 8.

Independent Activity

Place Value

100 Chart Paths

Warm-up
Name any two-digit number. What number is 10 more than your number? 10 less? Try this a few more times with different numbers.

Number of Players: 4 (in teams of 2)

Goal: Make a path from one side of the 100 Chart to the other.

Materials: 2 sets of digit cards (0–9)

100 Chart gameboard (page 31)

Markers in 2 different colors (12 of each color)

Game Rules

1. Mix both sets of cards.
Stack the cards facedown.

2. Team A picks 2 cards and makes a two-digit number.
They cover the number on the gameboard.
What number is 10 more than that number? 1 more? 1 less?
Team A chooses one of those numbers.
They cover it on the gameboard.

> *Example:* Players pick 2 and 7.
> They cover 27 on the board.
> They say, "1 less than 27 is 26."
> Then they cover 26.

3. Teams take turns.

4. The game ends when one team makes a path from one side of the gameboard to the other. That team wins the game.

1	2	3	4	5	6	7	8	9	10
11	12	13	14	15	16	17	18	19	20
21	22	23	24	25	26	27	28	29	30
31	32	33	34	35	36	37	38	39	40
41	42	43	44	45	46	47	48	49	50
51	52	53	54	55	56	57	58	59	60
61	62	63	64	65	66	67	68	69	70
71	72	73	74	75	76	77	78	79	80
81	82	83	84	85	86	87	88	89	90
91	92	93	94	95	96	97	98	99	100

Make It Harder: Teams find numbers that are 20 more/less and 2 more/less than their number.

Don't Forget: Play this game over and over to help you do better on skill checks and other activities.

100 Chart

1	2	3	4	5	6	7	8	9	10
11	12	13	14	15	16	17	18	19	20
21	22	23	24	25	26	27	28	29	30
31	32	33	34	35	36	37	38	39	40
41	42	43	44	45	46	47	48	49	50
51	52	53	54	55	56	57	58	59	60
61	62	63	64	65	66	67	68	69	70
71	72	73	74	75	76	77	78	79	80
81	82	83	84	85	86	87	88	89	90
91	92	93	94	95	96	97	98	99	100

Date _____

Skill Check 9

STOP Don't start yet! Star two problems that may have answers greater than 45.

Fill in the missing numbers from the 100 chart.

1. [ ] [42]
   [ ]

2. [34]
   [ ] [ ]

3. Order these numbers from least to greatest. 35, 53, 47 _____

4. forty-nine _____ **5.** thirty-eight _____ **6.** 3 tens more than 35 _____

Use two of the digits 2, 3, and 5 to form these numbers.

7. even number between 50 and 60 _____ **8.** odd number greater than 40 _____

9. even number less than 40 _____ **10.** odd number between 30 and 40 _____

Go On What numbers come next? 43, 53, 63, _____, _____

Date _____

Skill Check 10

STOP Don't start yet! Star a problem that may have an answer less than 30.

Fill in the missing numbers from the 100 chart.

1. [ ] [ ]
   [ ] [52]

2. [ ]
   [ ]
   [67]

3. Order these numbers from least to greatest. 48, 42, 52 _____

4. thirty-six _____ **5.** twenty-seven _____ **6.** 3 tens more than 26 _____

Use two of the digits 4, 5, and 6 to form these numbers.

7. odd number between 60 and 70 _____ **8.** even number greater than 60 _____

9. odd number less than 50 _____ **10.** even number between 40 and 50 _____

Go On Which number is closest to 54? Explain. 51, 45, 55, 50 _____

What Numbers Are Missing? A

Write the missing numbers. Use the numbers shown in this 100 chart to help you.

What Numbers Are Missing? B

Each exercise is a piece of the 100 chart. Write the missing numbers.

1.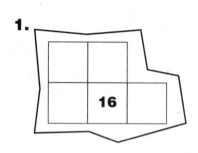

2.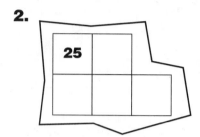

3.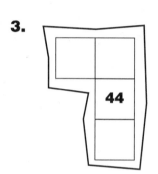

4.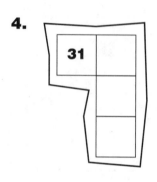

5.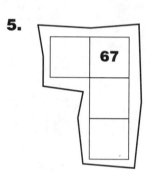

6.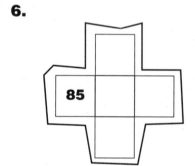

7.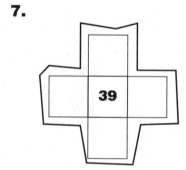

8.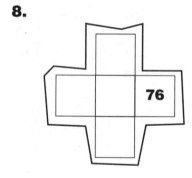

9.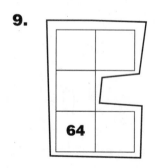

10.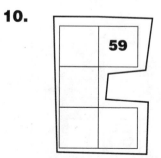

11.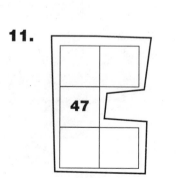

Independent Activity

Staircase Number Puzzle A

Use the clues to solve the puzzle and discover a fun fact.

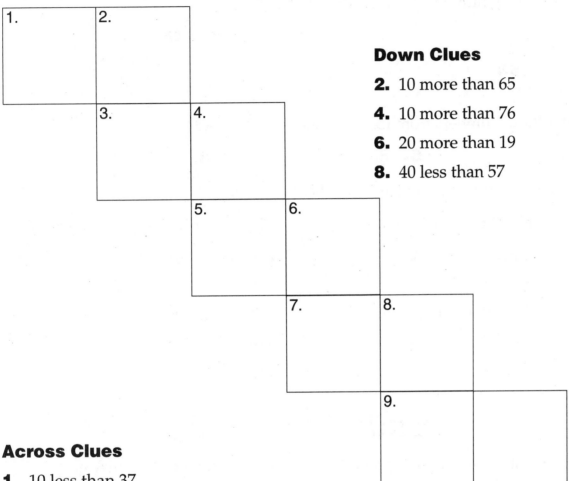

Down Clues

2. 10 more than 65

4. 10 more than 76

6. 20 more than 19

8. 40 less than 57

Across Clues

1. 10 less than 37

3. 20 more than 38

5. 30 less than 93

7. 40 more than 51

9. 100 less than 177

Fun Fact: Number 8 down tells the number of muscles used to smile.

Date _____

Skill Check 11

STOP Don't start yet! Star the problem that may have the least answer.

Fill in the missing numbers from the 100 chart.

1.

	63

2.

45	

3. Order these numbers from least to greatest. 62, 26, 45 _____

4. sixty-one _____   **5.** fifty-six _____   **6.** 3 tens more than 32 _____

Use two of the digits 3, 4, and 8 to form these numbers.

7. odd number between 40 and 50 _____   **8.** odd number greater than 50 _____

9. even number less than 35 _____   **10.** even number between 40 and 50 _____

Go On → What other number belongs?

58	54	52

Date _____

Skill Check 12

STOP Don't start yet! Star the problem that may have the greatest answer.

Fill in the missing numbers from the 100 chart.

1.

71	

2.

58	

3. Order these numbers from least to greatest. 57, 37, 34 _____

4. fifty-two _____   **5.** forty-four _____   **6.** 3 tens more than _____

Use two of the digits 5, 6, and 8 to form these numbers.

7. odd number between 60 and 70 _____   **8.** odd number greater than 80 _____

9. even number less than 57 _____   **10.** even number between 66 and 76 _____

Go On → Write a two-digit number with digits that add up to 9. _____

Creating Numbers A

Use two of the three digits in the box for each answer.
Hint: Use digit cards to help you make two-digit numbers.

Use 1, 2, or 4.

1. Make a two-digit number less than 20. _____

2. Make an odd two-digit number. _____

3. Make a number greater than 35. _____

4. Make the greatest possible two-digit number. _____

Use 2, 4, or 7.

5. Make the number that is ten more than 32. _____

6. Make an odd number between 40 and 50. _____

7. Make the least possible two-digit number. _____

Use 4, 7, or 9.

8. Make the number that is ten less than 84. _____

9. Make an odd number less than 60. _____

10. Make the greatest possible even two-digit number. _____

What Numbers Are Missing? C

Each exercise is a piece of a 100 chart. Write the missing numbers.

1.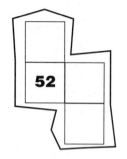

2.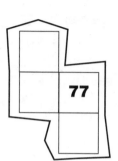

3.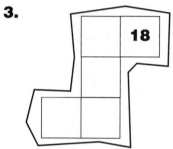

4.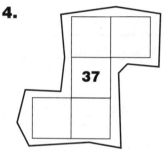

5.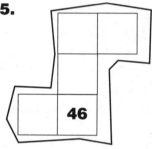

6.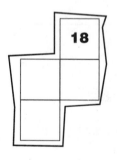

7.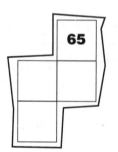

8.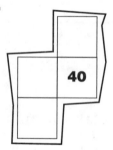

9.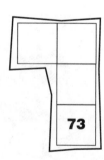

10.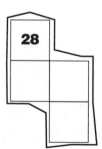

11.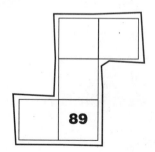

Independent Activity

Staircase Number Puzzle B

Use the clues to solve the puzzle and discover a fun fact.

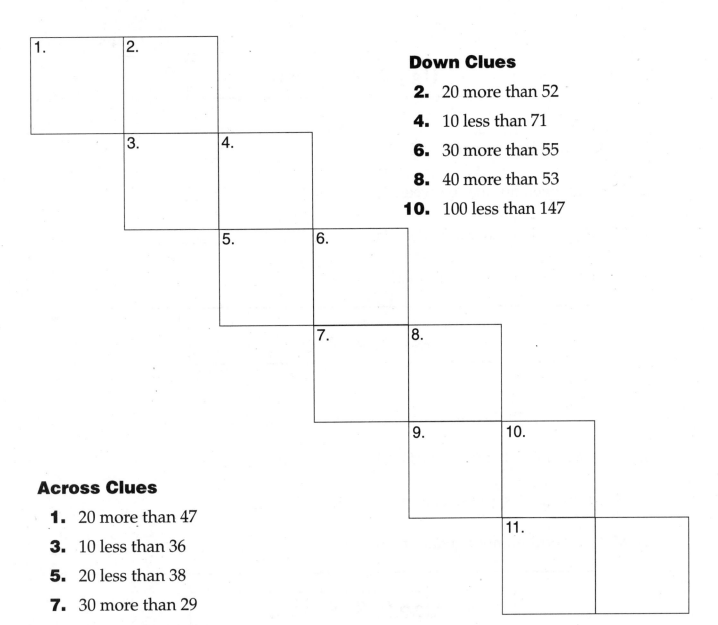

Down Clues

2. 20 more than 52

4. 10 less than 71

6. 30 more than 55

8. 40 more than 53

10. 100 less than 147

Across Clues

1. 20 more than 47

3. 10 less than 36

5. 20 less than 38

7. 30 more than 29

9. See Fun Fact below.

11. 100 less than 171

Fun Fact: Number 9 across is the number of muscles used to frown.

Creating Numbers B

Use three of the four digits in the box for each answer.
Hint: Use digit cards to help you make three-digit numbers.

Use 2, 3, 4, or 6.

1. Make a number greater than 550. _____

2. Make an even number between 300 and 500. _____

3. Make an odd number less than 300. _____

4. Make the least possible number. _____

Use 1, 4, 7, or 8.

5. Make an odd number less than 400. _____

6. Make a number between 700 and 800. _____

7. Make the greatest possible even number. _____

8. Make an odd number greater than 800. _____

Use 2, 3, 5, or 9.

9. Make a number between 500 and 700. _____

10. Make an even number less than 400. _____

11. Make an odd number between 300 and 500. _____

12. Make the greatest possible even number. _____

Addition

19 Plus

Warm-up
What are the sums for 19 + 8
19 + 5, 19 + 7, and 19 + 3?
What is an easy way to add 1
to a number? Explain.

Number of Players: 2

Goal: Cover three in a row on the gameboard.

Materials: 2 sets of digit cards (4–9 only)

19 Plus gameboard (page 43)

Markers in 2 different colors (12 of each color)

Game Rules

1. Mix both sets of cards.
Stack the cards facedown.

2. The first player shows the top card.
He or she adds 19 to the number.
The player says the number sentence and covers the sum
on the board.

> *Example:* The player picks 7 and says, "19 plus 7 equals 26."
> He or she covers 26 on the gameboard.

3. Players take turns.

4. The game ends when one player covers three in a row.
That player wins the game.

Make It Harder: Players use the *28 Plus* gameboard (page 44).
They pick number cards and add 28.

Don't Forget: Play this game over and over to help
you do better on skill checks and other activities.

$$\begin{array}{r} 19 \\ +\ 7 \\ \hline 26 \end{array}$$

26	**24**	**23**	**27**
25	**28**	**26**	**23**
26	**27**	**25**	**28**
23	**28**	**27**	**24**

19 Plus

26	24	23	27
25	28	26	23
26	27	25	28
23	28	27	24

$19 + 7 = ?$

7

28 Plus

32	**34**	**36**	**35**
35	**33**	**34**	**37**
34	**36**	**35**	**33**
33	**32**	**37**	**36**

28 + 8 = ?

8

Game

Skill Check 13

STOP Don't start yet! Star two problems that may have even answers.

1. $16 + 5 =$ _____

2. $24 + 6 + 3 =$ _____

3. $53 + 9 =$ _____

4. $34 + 8 =$ _____

5. $45 + 23 =$ _____

6. $56 + 6 =$ _____

7.
$$\begin{array}{r} 78 \\ +\ 9 \\ \hline \end{array}$$

8.
$$\begin{array}{r} 25 \\ +\ 37 \\ \hline \end{array}$$

9.
$$\begin{array}{r} 36 \\ +\ 49 \\ \hline \end{array}$$

10.
$$\begin{array}{r} 167 \\ +\ 8 \\ \hline \end{array}$$

Go On Write three addition sentences that equal 35.

_____

Date _____

Skill Check 14

STOP Don't start yet! Star two problems that may have the greatest answers.

1. $17 + 6 =$ _____

2. $23 + 2 + 7 =$ _____

3. $42 + 9 =$ _____

4. $63 + 8 =$ _____

5. $35 + 33 =$ _____

6. $48 + 7 =$ _____

7.
$$\begin{array}{r} 68 \\ +\ 6 \\ \hline \end{array}$$

8.
$$\begin{array}{r} 38 \\ +\ 24 \\ \hline \end{array}$$

9.
$$\begin{array}{r} 53 \\ +\ 38 \\ \hline \end{array}$$

10.
$$\begin{array}{r} 148 \\ +\ 5 \\ \hline \end{array}$$

Go On Which numbers come next? 14, 20, 26, 32, _____, _____

Addition Trees A

Write the missing numbers. The first one is done for you.

1.

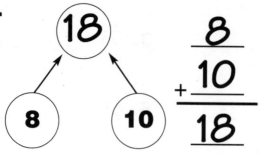

$$\begin{array}{r} 8 \\ + \ 10 \\ \hline 18 \end{array}$$

2.

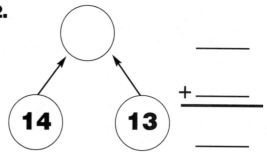

3.

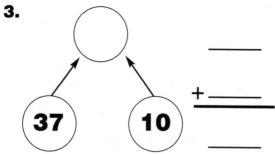

4.

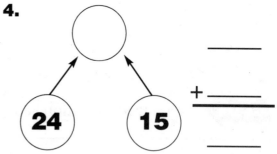

5.

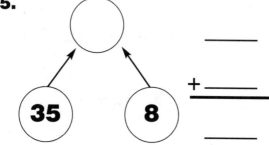

6.

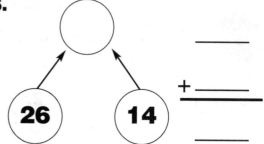

7.

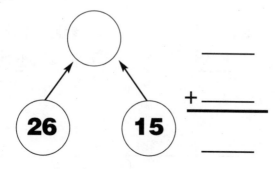

8. Make your own addition tree.

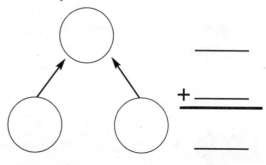

Independent Activity

Making Sums A

Use the numbers in the box. Create an addition problem for each sum.

1.

20	40
10	16

_____ + _____ = 36   _____ + _____ = 60

_____ + _____ = 50   _____ + _____ = 56

2.

35	10
15	30

_____ + _____ = 45   _____ + _____ = 40

_____ + _____ = 50   _____ + _____ = 65

3.

25	10
30	8

_____ + _____ = 40   _____ + _____ = 33

_____ + _____ = 55   _____ + _____ = 38

4.

40	20
15	9

_____ + _____ = 35   _____ + _____ = 24

_____ + _____ = 49   _____ + _____ = 60

Make a *new sum* using two of the numbers in the box above.

_____ + _____ = _____

Date _____

Skill Check 15

 STOP Don't start yet! Star two problems that may answers less than 50.

1. 16 + 6 = _____   **2.** 35 + 5 + 4 = _____   **3.** 26 + 6 = _____

4. 44 + 7 = _____   **5.** 54 + 35 = _____   **6.** 66 + 8 = _____

7. 59
      + 7
      ‾‾‾

8. 47
      + 26
      ‾‾‾

9. 39
      + 48
      ‾‾‾

10. 156
      + 6
      ‾‾‾

Go On ▶ What numbers come next? 13, 18, 23, 28, _____, _____

Date _____

Skill Check 16

 STOP Don't start yet! Star two problems that may have odd answers.

1. 18 + 4 = _____   **2.** 43 + 4 + 3 = _____   **3.** 36 + 6 = _____

4. 56 + 7 = _____   **5.** 64 + 34 = _____   **6.** 37 + 9 = _____

7. 49
      + 8
      ‾‾‾

8. 46
      + 35
      ‾‾‾

9. 58
      + 39
      ‾‾‾

10. 175
      + 7
      ‾‾‾

Go On ▶ Write another number sentence that belongs in the box. Explain your answer.

30 + 15 =	28 + 17 =
23 + 22 =	

48   **Skill Checks**

Addition Trees B

Write the missing numbers. The first one is done for you.

1.
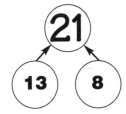

2.
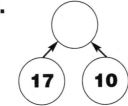

3.
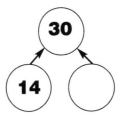

4.
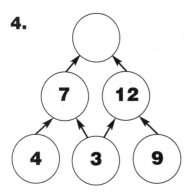

5.
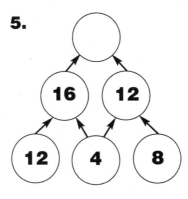

6.
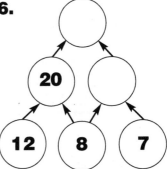

7.
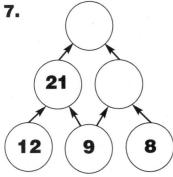

8.
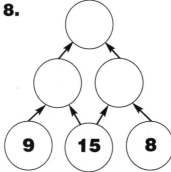

9.
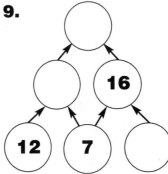

10.
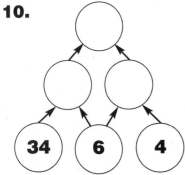

11. Make your own addition tree.
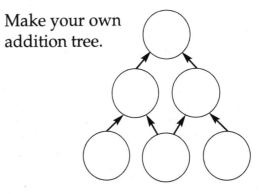

Making Sums B

Use the numbers in the box.
Create an addition problem for each sum.

1.

10	15
30	8

_____ + _____ = 25   _____ + _____ = 45

_____ + _____ = 23   _____ + **10** + _____ = 48

2.

15	30
20	7

_____ + _____ = 50   _____ + _____ = 22

_____ + _____ = 35   **15** + _____ + _____ = 52

3.

_____ + _____ = 47   _____ + _____ = 27

40	12
35	15

_____ + _____ = 52   _____ + _____ + **10** = 60

_____ + _____ = 75   _____ + **15** + _____ = 67

4.

40	30
25	11

_____ + _____ = 36   _____ + _____ + **10** = 80

_____ + _____ = 65   **10** + _____ + _____ = 51

Make a *new sum* using three of the numbers in the box above.

_____ + _____ + _____ = _____

Subtraction

Difference Bingo

Number of Players: 4 (in 2 teams)

Goal: Cover three in a row on the gameboard.

Materials: 2 sets of digit cards (1–5 only)
Difference Bingo gameboard (page 53)
Markers in 2 different colors (12 of each color)

Game Rules

1. Mix both sets of cards.
Stack the cards facedown.

2. The first team picks 4 cards.
They make two 2-digit numbers and subtract.
Players cover the difference if it is on the gameboard.
If not, players keep trying different numbers with the
same cards.
They pass the turn if the differences they find are not
on the board.

3. Teams take turns.

4. The game ends when one team covers three in a row.
That team wins the game.

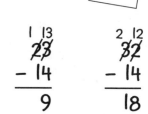

Make It Harder: Teams pick 5 cards.
They use only four of the cards.

Don't Forget: Play this game over and over
to help you do better on skill checks and
other activities.

8	7	0	9
0	9	3	1
8	2	7	9
6	9	1	8

Difference Bingo

8	7	0	9
0	9	3	1
8	2	7	9
6	9	1	8

Game

Date _____

Skill Check 17

 Don't start yet! Star three problems that have may even answers.

1. 37 – 4 = _____

2. 74 – 40 = _____

3. 47 – 9 = _____

4. _____ + 12 = 20

5. 34 – 19 = _____

6. 53 – 7 = _____

7.   60
      – 43
      ‾‾‾‾

8.   73
      – 38
      ‾‾‾‾

9.   164
      – 7
      ‾‾‾‾

10.   280
       – 46
       ‾‾‾‾

 What number comes next? 69, 67, 65, _____
Identify the pattern.

Date _____

Skill Check 18

 Don't start yet! Star two problems that may have answers between 20 and 40.

1. 28 – 5 = _____

2. 67 – 30 = _____

3. 53 – 8 = _____

4. 16 + _____ = 20

5. 45 – 29 = _____

6. 64 – 8 = _____

7.   40
      – 28
      ‾‾‾‾

8.   66
      – 39
      ‾‾‾‾

9.   176
       – 8
       ‾‾‾‾

10.   260
       – 38
       ‾‾‾‾

 Which number is closer to 75— 69 or 79? Explain.

Rearrange and Find A

Write 2, 3, and 6 in the squares to make each difference.
The first one is done for you. **Hint:** Use digit cards to help you.

1.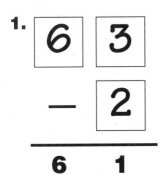

6 1

2.

2 3

3.

3 4

4.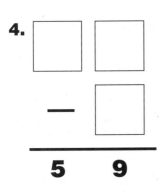

5 9

5.

1 7

6.

2 6

Write 3, 5, and 6 in the squares to make each difference.

7.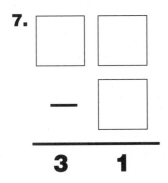

3 1

8.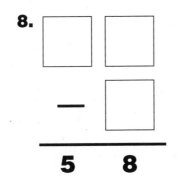

5 8

9.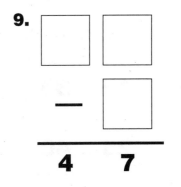

4 7

Finding Pairs A

Use the numbers in the box.
Create a subtraction problem for each difference.

1.

72	42
32	22

_____ – _____ = 10   _____ – _____ = 30

_____ – _____ = 20   _____ – _____ = 40

2.

50	25
30	15

_____ – _____ = 5   _____ – _____ = 15

_____ – _____ = 10   _____ – _____ = 25

3.

53	23
33	9

_____ – _____ = 30   _____ – _____ = 24

_____ – _____ = 14   _____ – _____ = 44

---

4. Make two **differences** using the numbers in the box.

46	36
26	40

_____ – _____ = _____

_____ – _____ = _____

Independent Activity

Date _____

Skill Check 19

 STOP Don't start yet! Star three problems that may have even answers.

1. $36 - 4 =$ _____   **2.** $58 - 20 =$ _____   **3.** $62 - 9 =$ _____

4. _____ $+ 14 = 20$ **5.** $36 - 29 =$ _____   **6.** $54 - 6 =$ _____

7.
$$\begin{array}{r} 50 \\ -26 \\ \hline \end{array}$$

8.
$$\begin{array}{r} 54 \\ -35 \\ \hline \end{array}$$

9.
$$\begin{array}{r} 183 \\ -8 \\ \hline \end{array}$$

10.
$$\begin{array}{r} 250 \\ -24 \\ \hline \end{array}$$

Go On ▶ What number is missing? 59, 55, 51, _____ , 43, 39

Date _____

Skill Check 20

 STOP Don't start yet! Star two problems that may have odd answers.

1. $28 - 6 =$ _____   **2.** $45 - 10 =$ _____   **3.** $76 - 8 =$ _____

4. $9 +$ _____ $= 20$ **5.** $41 - 19 =$ _____   **6.** $66 - 9 =$ _____

7.
$$\begin{array}{r} 30 \\ -17 \\ \hline \end{array}$$

8.
$$\begin{array}{r} 43 \\ -28 \\ \hline \end{array}$$

9.
$$\begin{array}{r} 157 \\ -9 \\ \hline \end{array}$$

10.
$$\begin{array}{r} 270 \\ -37 \\ \hline \end{array}$$

Go On ▶ Write three subtraction sentences that equal 26.

Rearrange and Find B

Write 2, 3, and 4 in the squares to make each sum or difference.
Write + or – in the circles. The first one is done for you.
Hint: Use digit cards to help you.

1.

$$\begin{array}{cc} 2 & 4 \\ - & 3 \end{array}$$

2 **1**

2.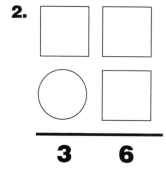

3 **6**

3.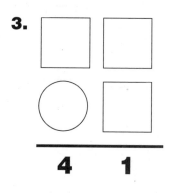

4 **1**

4.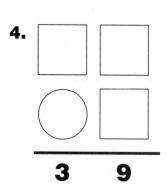

3 **9**

5.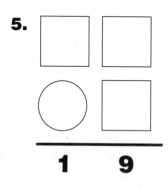

1 **9**

6.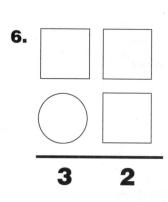

3 **2**

7.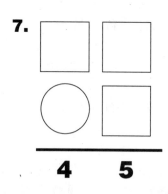

4 **5**

8.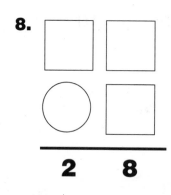

2 **8**

9.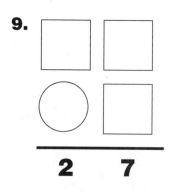

2 **7**

Independent Activity

Finding Pairs B

Use the numbers in the box. Create a subtraction problem for each difference.

1.

85	60
35	15

_____ – _____ = 50   _____ – _____ = 20

_____ – _____ = 70   _____ – _____ = 45

2.

62	42
32	8

_____ – _____ = 30   _____ – _____ = 34

_____ – _____ = 54   _____ – _____ = 24

3.

53	43
23	5

_____ – _____ = 20   _____ – _____ = 38

_____ – _____ = 48   _____ – _____ = 18

4.

71	41
31	4

_____ – _____ = 27   _____ – _____ = 30

_____ – _____ = 67   _____ – _____ = 37

Make two **differences** using the numbers in the box.

5.

73	33
23	9

_____ – _____ = _____

_____ – _____ = _____

23 – 9 = ?

Subtraction Squares C

Subtract each row and column to find the missing numbers.
The first one is done for you.

17-13=16-12

1.

36	20	*16*
19	7	*12*
17	*13*	*4*

2.

39	24	
16	9	

3.

55	29	
23	15	

4.

41	34	
29	25	

5.

67	38	
24	16	

6.

44	25	
18	9	

7.

52	21	
26	14	

8.

29	13	
16	8	

9.

60	15	
27	8	

Independent Activity

Rearrange and Find C

Write 3, 5, 8, or 9 in the squares to make each sum or difference.
Write + or − in the circles. **Hint:** Use digit cards to help you.

1.

☐ ☐
○ ☐
_____
4   3

2.

☐ ☐
○ ☐
_____
2   6

3.

☐ ☐
○ ☐
_____
9   4

4.

☐ ☐
○ ☐
_____
6   2

5.

☐ ☐
○ ☐
_____
4   4

6.

☐ ☐
○ ☐
_____
7   8

7.

☐ ☐
○ ☐
_____
4   5

8.

☐ ☐
○ ☐
_____
7   4

9.

☐ ☐
○ ☐
_____
2   7

Subtraction Squares D

Subtract each row and column to find the missing numbers.
The first one is done for you.

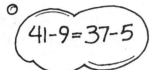

41-9=37-5

1.

60	19	41
23	14	9
37	5	32

2.

79	23	
44	15	

3.

70	38	
46	18	

4.

80	36	
53	19	

5.

61	34	
48	25	

6.

92	35	
29	16	

7.

71	29	
43	17	

8.

90	44	
51	32	

9.

87	25	
39	18	

Digit Cards

0	1	2	3
4	5	<u>6</u>	7
8	<u>9</u>	0	1
2	3	4	5
<u>6</u>	7	8	<u>9</u>